This book belongs to:

Lauren

Contents

Some words appear in **bold** in this book.
Turn to the glossary to learn about them.

Mad about...
Ballet

written by Lisa Regan
illustrated by Sue Hendra and Paul Linnet

consultant: Dawn King LCDD, RAD, RTS
Director of Gedling Ballet School

Welcome to the ballet

Ballet is a beautiful form of dancing. It tells stories to music. Ballet began about 500 years ago, in Italy.

Ballet became very popular in France 400 years ago. That is why many of the words used to describe ballet are French.

Ballet dancers have very fit bodies. They can balance and bend far more than any ordinary person.

A **choreographer** (*kor-ee-og-raf-er*) is the person in charge of planning the dance moves in a ballet.

The word 'ballet' is also used to describe a performance. People say they are 'going to the ballet'.

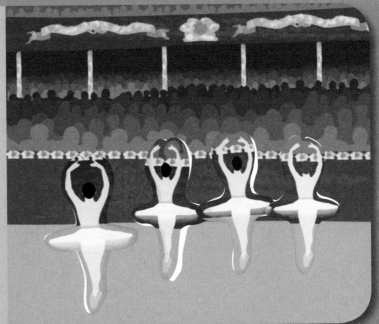

Getting started

Children can begin to learn ballet when they are very young. As dancers grow older, they learn harder moves. To become a **professional**, dancers train very hard, usually from the age of ten.

A ballet class always begins with exercises to warm up the dancers' muscles. Dancers also perform gentle stretches.

A ballet dancer's **posture** is very important. A dancer's body should stretch upwards at all times.

bad posture

good posture

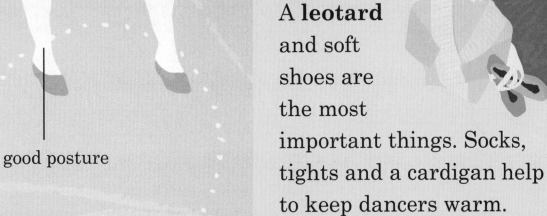

Very little is needed to start ballet. A **leotard** and soft shoes are the most important things. Socks, tights and a cardigan help to keep dancers warm.

Basic positions

One of the first things a ballet dancer learns is the basic **positions**. These are five foot and arm **poses**.

First position

Arms are held in a gentle, curved position

Legs are turned outwards from the hips

When children first learn ballet they do not stand with their legs and feet fully turned out. This takes some time to learn.

Toes and feet are turned outwards

Heels are kept together

Second position

Arms should be held wide

The elbows are slightly curved and not too low

If you have a computer, you can download a poster of ballet moves from www.ladybird.com/madabout

To move from first position into second position, keep the feet at the same angle. Keep a space between the feet

First and second position are simple. They can both be practised in front of a mirror at home.

Harder positions

The basic positions get harder and harder. Some teachers start with the arms, then move on to the foot positions later.

Third position

One arm is held in first position and one in second

Fourth position

The front arm is held above the head in a graceful curve. The other arm is still held to the side

One foot is placed in front of the other. The front heel should be halfway along the back foot

One foot is positioned exactly in front of the other, with a space between the feet

Fifth position

Both arms are held above the head

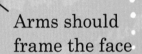

Arms should frame the face

The feet move together from fourth position to fifth position

Feet should be crossed, with legs turned outwards

Practice makes perfect

A dance studio has a rail on the wall called a **barre** (*bar*). Dancers hold onto the *barre* when stretching, balancing and practising ballet moves.

barre

Legs bend during a *plié* or *demi-plié*

Leg bends are called **pliés** (PLEE-*ays*) and half leg bends **demi-pliés**. They are the first moves a dancer learns.

Ballet movements should be done with pointed feet. That makes a dancer's legs look longer and more graceful.

straight back ————

feet pointed

legs stretched in front

The **pirouette** (*pi-roo-ET*) is a favourite move. Dancers perform it by spinning on one leg.

With skill and practice, almost every ballet move can be performed **en tournant** (*on-TOOR-non*), or turning. That allows the dancer to move around the floor.

Dancing together

When two people dance together it is called **pas de deux** (*pa-de-DUH*). Together, the dancers can perform incredible steps and lifts.

An **arabesque** (*a-reb-ESK*) is a wonderful ballet balance. The male dancer sometimes supports the female in an *arabesque* **en pointe** (*on-point*), which means on tiptoes.

en pointe

The male dancer
must be very
strong, so he can
hold his partner
in the air.

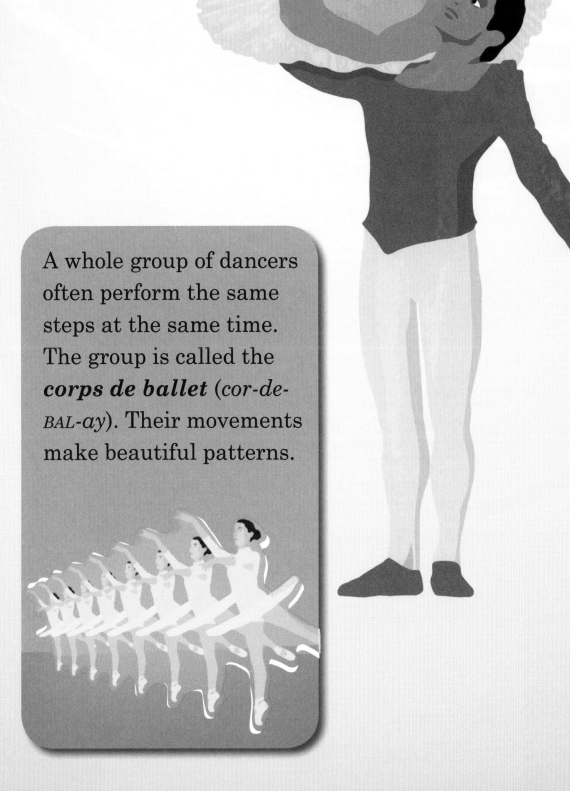

A whole group of dancers
often perform the same
steps at the same time.
The group is called the
corps de ballet (*cor-de-
BAL-ay*). Their movements
make beautiful patterns.

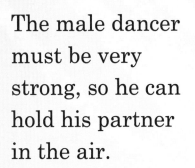

Ballet shoes

Dancers wear ballet shoes made of leather, satin or canvas when they first begin their training. The shoes are held on the feet with elastic or ribbons.

A dancer must learn to tie his or her ballet shoes properly. This can take some practice. Both ribbons are crossed in front of and behind the leg, near the ankle. They should be tied neatly on the inside of the leg.

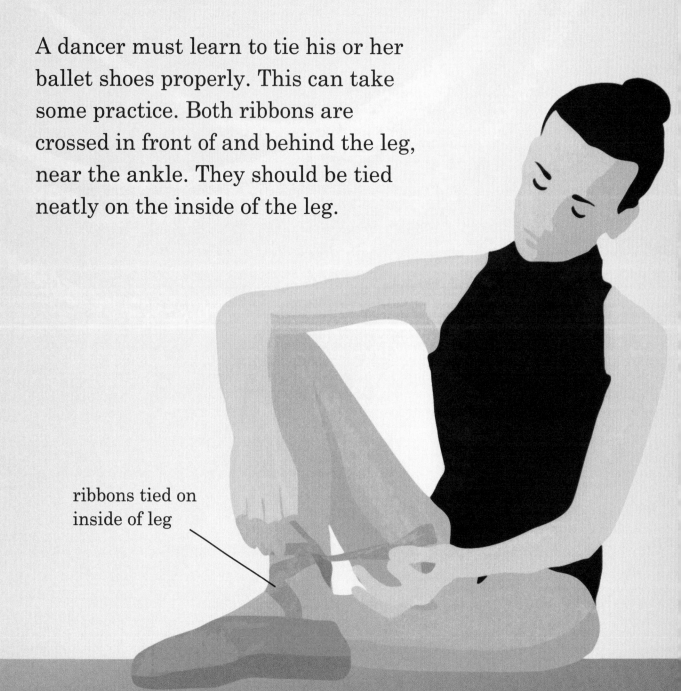

ribbons tied on inside of leg

Special *pointe* shoes are needed to dance *en pointe*. They have hard toes and strong **soles**. *Pointe* shoes can be painful to wear if they do not fit correctly. Some dancers use padding to protect their toes inside the shoe.

ribbons are hand-sewn onto shoes and then cut to the right length

teacher

pupil

Teachers can tell when their pupils' feet and bodies are strong enough to work *en pointe*.

Ballet school

Ballet school is for dancers who want to move on from ballet classes and learn more. An audition, or test, must be passed before a dancer is offered a place at ballet school.

Dancers must keep their hair tidy. Long hair is tied back so it does not fall across the dancer's face or eyes.

Ballet teachers help their pupils to warm up. They might play games to warm up, such as pretending to be animals or fairy tale **characters**.

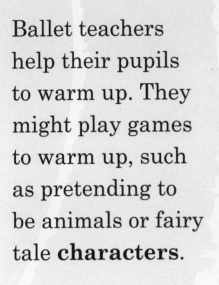

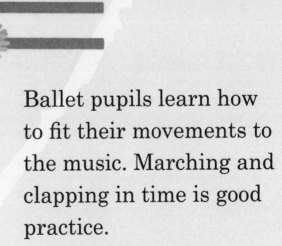

Ballet pupils learn how to fit their movements to the music. Marching and clapping in time is good practice.

Girl dancers **curtsey** to their teacher at the end of a class.

Ballet costumes

Ballet costumes are designed to tell the audience about the characters in a ballet. They also show off the movements of the dance.

This pretty net dress is called a *tutu* (*too-too*).

All ballet costumes are designed to help dancers move as easily as possible.

The costumes of the main characters in a ballet are often a different colour to the costumes of the other dancers. That makes the main characters stand out.

Some ballets use amazing costumes. In the ballet *The Tales of Beatrix Potter*, all the dancers are dressed in animal costumes.

Going to the ballet

A trip to the theatre to
see a ballet performance
is a magical experience.

Many **classical ballets**
tell traditional stories,
such as fairy tales.
Some ballets
tell love stories.

The Nutcracker
is a traditional
story

Modern ballets do not always have a story. Instead, the dancers use their movements to show feelings and **emotions**.

Ballet dancers use their body shapes and their faces to show their characters' feelings or what is happening in the story.

Famous ballets

Swan Lake
This ballet tells the story of
Princess Odette, who is turned
into a swan by a sorcerer.

The Nutcracker
A beautiful ballet about a magical
Christmas present.

The Dream
A ballet based on Shakespeare's
A Midsummer Night's Dream.

Sleeping Beauty
This famous ballet tells
the story of a princess woken
from a spell by the kiss
of a prince.

Romeo and Juliet

A romantic ballet based on Shakespeare's play.

Les Noces (The Wedding)

This ballet tells the story of a wedding in a poor Russian family nearly one hundred years ago.

The Four Temperaments

This is a modern ballet. It looks at different feelings, such as sadness and happiness.

The Prince of the Pagodas

This modern ballet tells the story of an ancient emperor and his daughters.

The Tales of Beatrix Potter

This ballet is based on the animal stories in Beatrix Potter's books.

Coppelia

In this ballet, a toymaker is tricked into thinking that one of his dolls has come to life.

Simply the best

Anna Pavlova

1881–1931
This Russian ballerina was famous for her graceful performances. She helped to design the *pointe* shoe used by most modern ballerinas.

Fonteyn and Nureyev

Dame Margot Fonteyn (1919–1991) and Rudolf Nureyev (1938–1993) danced beautifully alone, but together they were the world's most famous partnership.

Alicia Markova

1910–2004

This English *prima ballerina* (leading lady) formed her own ballet company in 1950. It later became the English National Ballet.

Vaslav Nijinsky

1890–1950

This male ballet dancer will always be remembered for his powerful body and great dance routines.

Darcey Bussell

1969–present

Darcey was 13 years old when she began serious training. She has shown that a ballet dancer can begin dancing when they are older and still become a great dancer.

Ballet positions

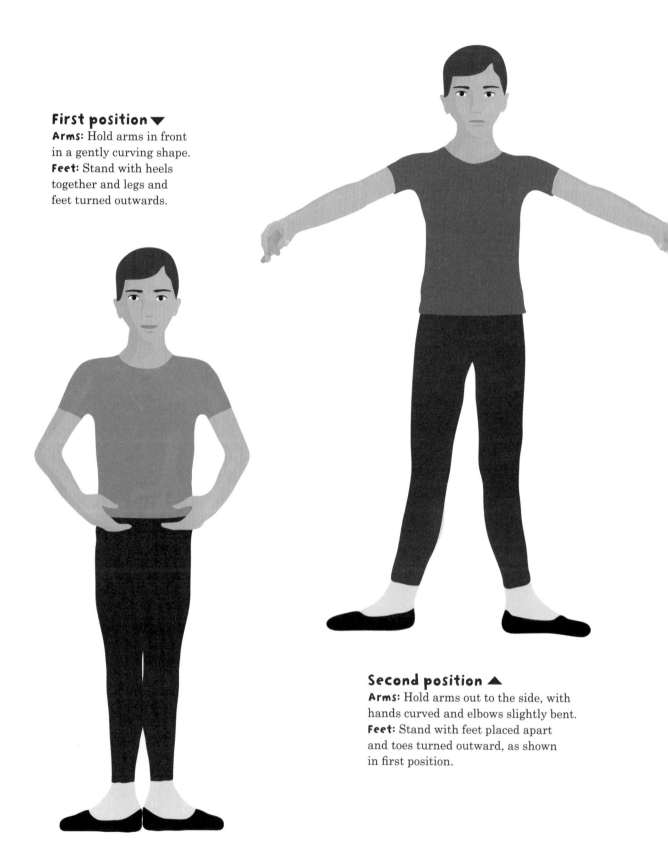

First position ▼
Arms: Hold arms in front
in a gently curving shape.
Feet: Stand with heels
together and legs and
feet turned outwards.

Second position ▲
Arms: Hold arms out to the side, with
hands curved and elbows slightly bent.
Feet: Stand with feet placed apart
and toes turned outward, as shown
in first position.

◀ Third position

Arms: Hold one arm in front (as shown in first position) and one arm at the side (as shown in second position).

Feet: One foot is placed halfway in front of the other. Toes turned outward as in first and second positions.

Fourth position ▶

Arms: Hold one arm out to the side (as in second position). The other arm is raised above the head, to form a gentle curve.

Feet: Place one foot in front of the other, with toes pointing in opposite directions. Keep a space between the back and the front foot.

Fifth position ▲

Arms: Hold both arms above the head to form an arch.

Feet: Feet are as shown in fourth position, but have no space between them.

31

Ballet movements

Pirouette

Plié

En pointe

32

Arabesque

Pas de deux

Mad about...
Ponies

written by Sandy Ransford
illustrated by Ian Escott

A pony's life

Ponies in the wild live in family groups called herds. The herd is made up of a male pony (the stallion), a number of female ponies (mares) and their foals. A pony is called a foal until it is one year old. Ponies are not fully grown until they are four or five years old. They may live until they are twenty-five to thirty years old or more.

Ponies spend most of their time eating grass.

Young foals drink
their mothers' milk.

If something frightens the ponies,
the herd can gallop away very fast.

Ponies and people

Ponies first lived on Earth about 65 million years ago. They were very different then. People began to keep ponies about 6,000 years ago, using them for pulling **chariots** in battles and for hunting wild animals. Later, ponies were ridden. For thousands of years, **horses** and ponies were the only form of transport on land.

The earliest pony was the size of a fox and had toes on its feet.

The Romans used ponies for chariot racing.

Strong, heavy horses were used for farm work. Before there were machines to help, horses pulled carts and ploughs.

Ladies rode side-saddle until recent times.

Points of a pony

The points of a horse or pony are the parts of its body that you can see. The difference between horses and ponies is that a horse is 14.3 **hands high** or taller, and a pony is up to 14.2 hands high.

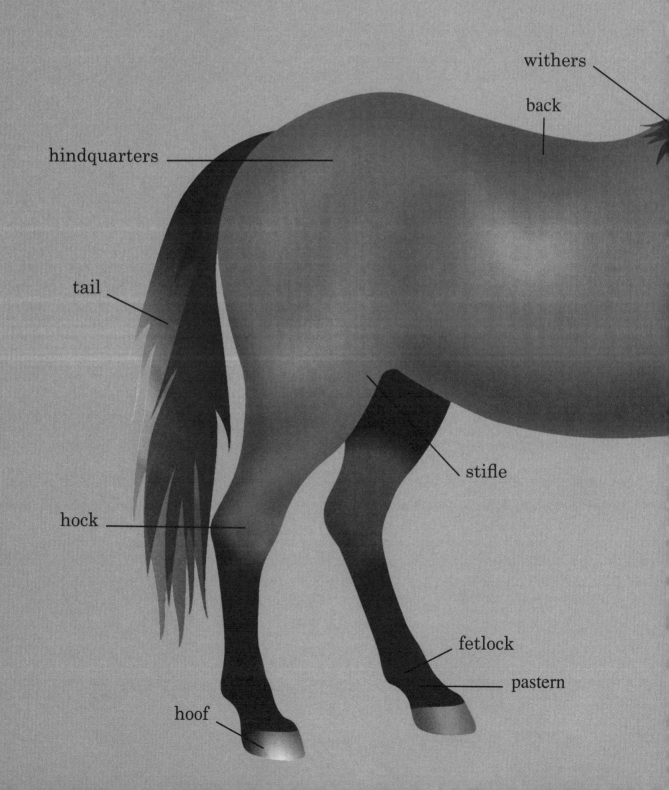

withers

back

hindquarters

tail

stifle

hock

fetlock

pastern

hoof

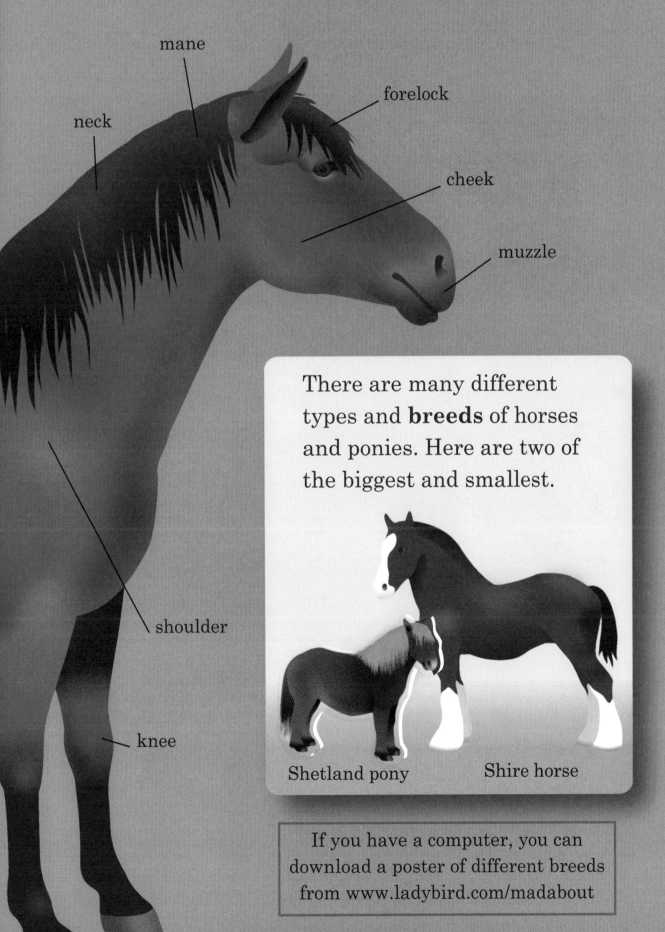

mane

neck

forelock

cheek

muzzle

shoulder

knee

There are many different types and **breeds** of horses and ponies. Here are two of the biggest and smallest.

Shetland pony

Shire horse

If you have a computer, you can download a poster of different breeds from www.ladybird.com/madabout

Colours and markings

Most ponies are brown, but each shade of brown has a different name.

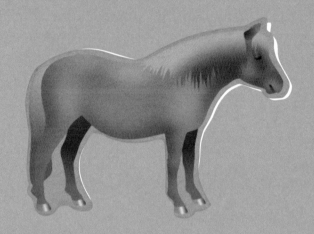

Chestnut ponies are a reddish-gold colour all over.

Bays are a red-brown colour with a black mane, tail and lower legs.

Brown ponies are dark brown with black manes and tails.

Piebald ponies have black and white patches all over.

Greys are dark or **dappled** when young and white when they get older.

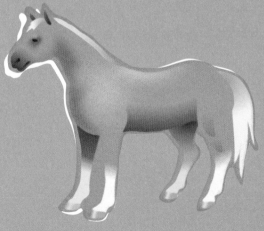

Palominos are gold-coloured, with a white mane and tail.

Ponies often have white markings on their faces and legs.

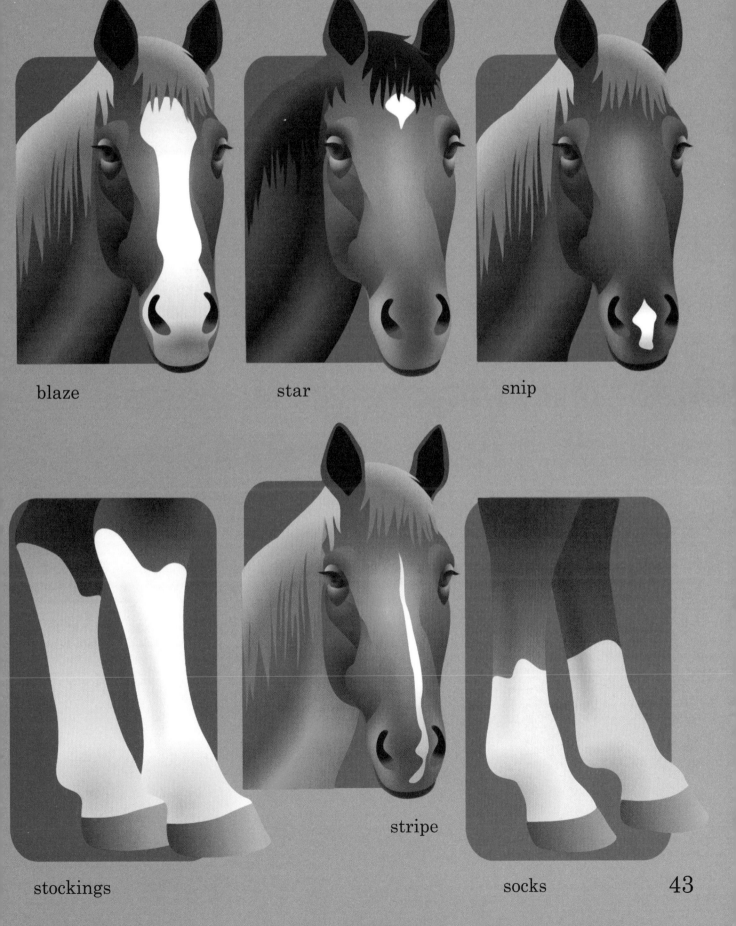

blaze

star

snip

stockings

stripe

socks

Where to keep a pony

You can keep a pony in a stable or a field. Many ponies spend half their time in the stable, and half out in the field. That way they get some shelter from the weather, and some freedom to graze and roam around.

A stable must be big enough for a pony to move about. Ponies need lots of fresh air, so the top half of the door should always be open.

A pony's field must be properly fenced. It needs a
clean water supply and some sort of shelter. This can
be thick hedges, shady trees or a field shelter.

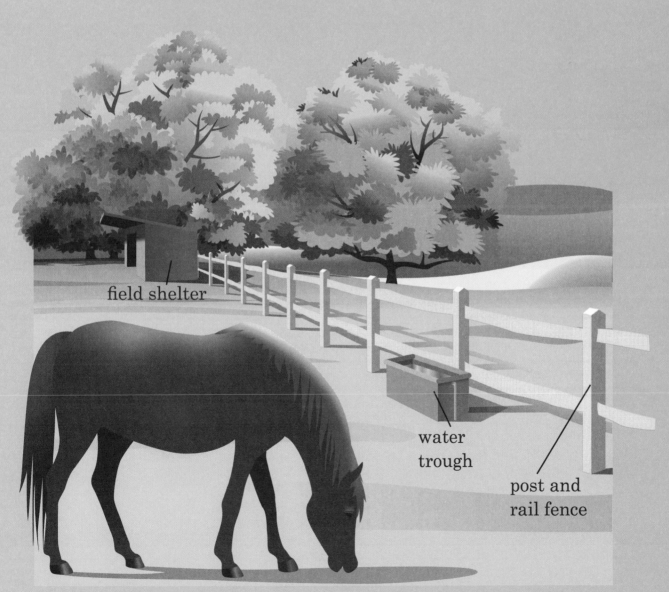

field shelter

water
trough

post and
rail fence

Handling a pony

Ponies are large, strong animals, but they are easy to handle. They like people to be quiet, calm and friendly. If you shout or rush about, it makes them nervous.

Meeting a pony
Speak to a pony in a friendly way and give it a pat on the neck.

In the stable

To get a pony to move in its stable, push on its hindquarters and say, "Get over."

Leading a pony

You lead a pony on its left-hand side. Hold the rope in both hands. Your right hand should be near its head and your left hand on the end of the rope.

47

Pony care

Ponies need a lot of looking after. They must be fed and groomed, and their stables cleaned out. They should always have fresh water nearby. Even if they live in a field they need checking twice a day.

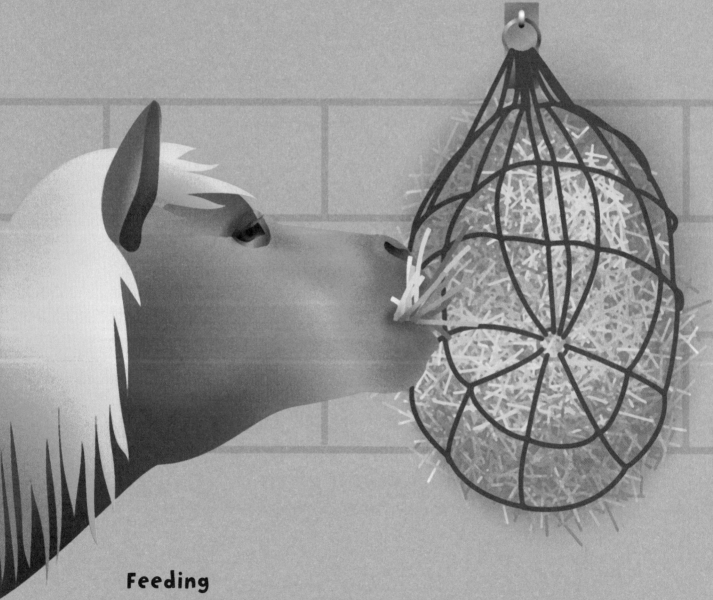

Feeding

In summer, ponies can live on grass. In winter, they need hay as well. They also need hay if they are kept in a stable. If they work hard, they need extra food, too.

Mucking out
Droppings and wet bedding must be cleaned out of the stable every day.

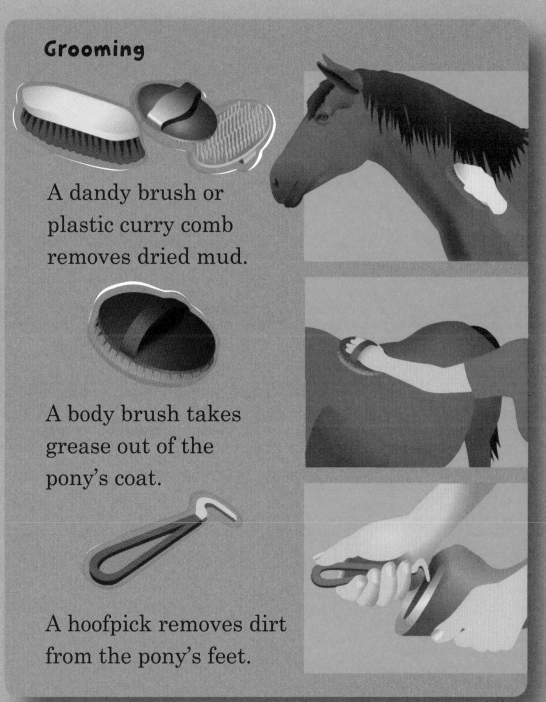

Grooming

A dandy brush or plastic curry comb removes dried mud.

A body brush takes grease out of the pony's coat.

A hoofpick removes dirt from the pony's feet.

Shoeing a pony

Ponies wear iron shoes to stop their hooves wearing down. But the hooves grow, like your nails, so every six to eight weeks the shoes must be taken off and the pony's feet trimmed. This is done by a **farrier**.

1 First the farrier cuts the nail ends, called clenches, that hold the shoe on the foot. He pulls off the shoe with pincers.

◀ **2** He trims the hoof. Then he **rasps** the surface smooth.

3 He heats the shoe in a ▶ furnace, then hammers it into shape on an **anvil**.

4 He tries the hot shoe on the pony's foot. It burns the hoof, making a lot of smoke, but the pony cannot feel it. ▶

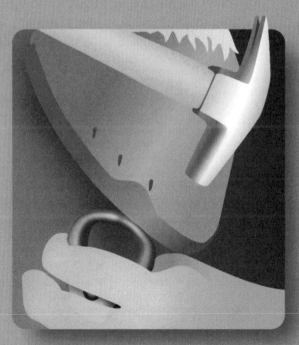

◀ **5** He cools the shoe in a bucket of cold water, then nails it on to the pony's foot.

6 The nails come out of the side of ▶ the hoof. The farrier twists off the ends of the nails, then hammers them down to form the clenches.

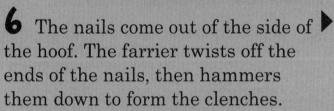

◀ **7** With the pony's foot resting on a tripod, the farrier rasps the hoof and clenches smooth.

A pony's tack

A pony's saddle, bridle, and other equipment it wears when it is ridden, is called **tack**. It is usually made of leather. Tack needs cleaning with **saddle soap** to keep it in good condition.

Snaffle bridle

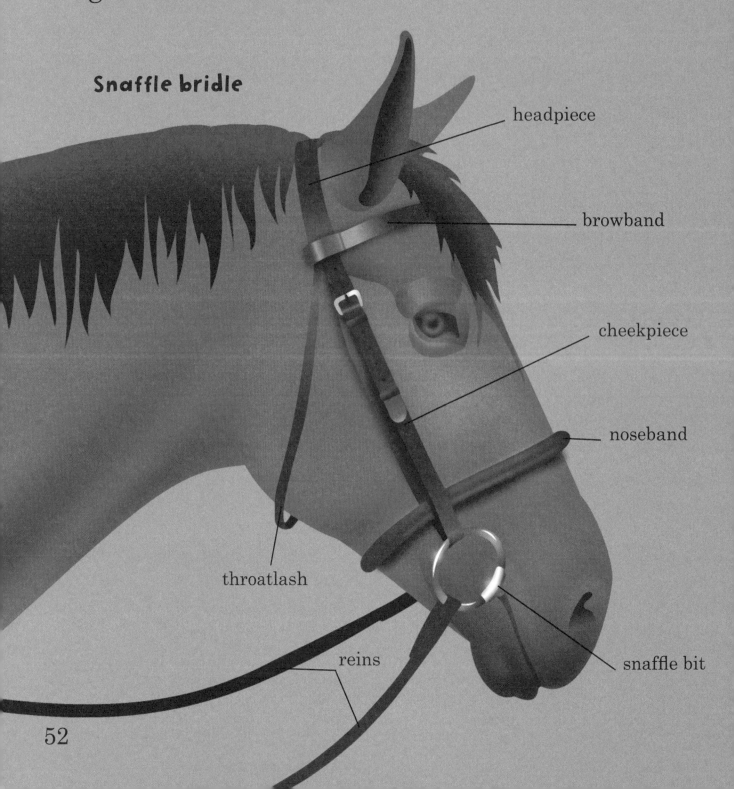

headpiece

browband

cheekpiece

noseband

throatlash

reins

snaffle bit

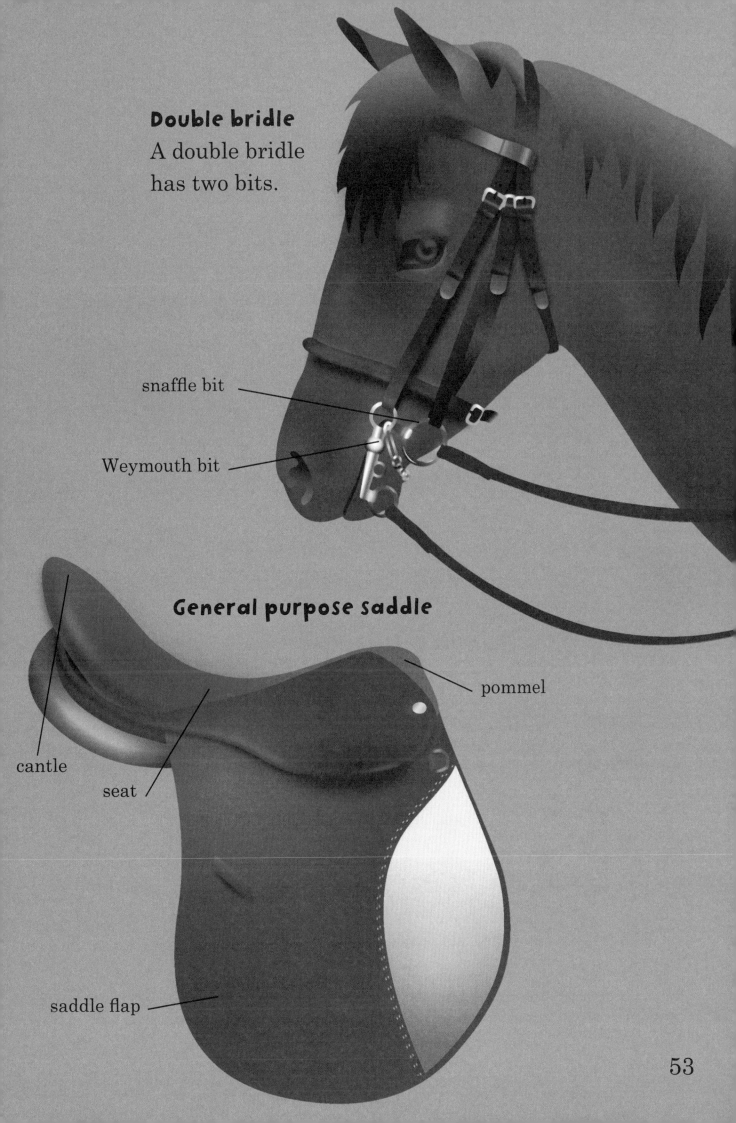

Double bridle
A double bridle
has two bits.

snaffle bit

Weymouth bit

General purpose saddle

pommel

cantle

seat

saddle flap

Riding clothes

When you ride a pony, you must wear a hard hat. **Jodhpurs** and boots are more comfortable than ordinary clothes.

To protect your head you need a riding hat or a skull cap. A skull cap may be covered by a colourful silk.

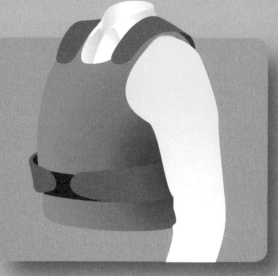

For jumping, you need a body protector to stop you hurting your back if you fall off.

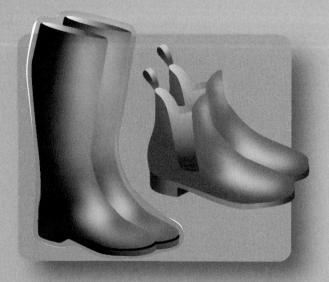

On your feet you can wear long riding boots or jodhpur boots. Long boots stop the stirrup leathers pinching your legs.

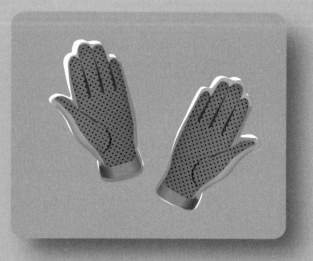

Riding gloves have rubber pimples on the palms so that you can hold the reins in wet weather.

A riding
hat has a
hard brim

You can
wear a smart
**hacking
jacket** or
a casual one

Jodhpurs stop your
legs getting rubbed

A pony's paces

Ponies have four natural **paces**, or ways in which they move forwards: walk, trot, canter and gallop. The walk is the slowest and the gallop the fastest.

Walk
You sit down in the saddle when a pony walks.

Trot

When a pony trots its feet hit the ground in diagonal pairs: left front and right hind, right front and left hind. You rise out of the saddle for one beat and sit for the other.

Canter

In the canter, the front and hind leg on one side are in front of those on the other. This is called the leading leg.

Gallop

When you gallop, you raise yourself out of the saddle and lean slightly forwards.

Riding activities

There are lots of ways you can enjoy riding. Going out for a ride in the countryside is called hacking. You may ride in an enclosed area, called a school, to improve your pony's paces and learn to jump. You could join a local riding club, and compete in events such as show jumping and **gymkhanas**.

Dressage needs a very well-schooled pony or horse.

The cross-country part of **eventing** involves galloping and jumping.

In a potato race, you have to pick up a potato, gallop down the field, and put it in a bucket – all from your pony's back.

59

Pony breeds

Australian ▲
Height: 12 to 14 hands high (122–142 centimetres)
Colour: Any solid colour
Did you know? The Australian pony breed
has existed for about 100 years.
It is a very good children's riding pony.

◀ New Forest
Height: one type is up to 13.1 hands high
(135 centimetres) and the other
13.2 to 14.2 hands high (137–147 centimetres)
Colour: Any solid colour
Did you know? From southern England, these ponies
are narrow in build and have good action. Together
with their range of heights, this makes them
excellent riding ponies for children of most ages.

Pony of the Americas ▶

Height: 11.2 to 13 hands high (117–132 centimetres)
Colour: Spotted
Did you know? This is a fairly new breed created in North America during the 1950s. It is a good children's riding pony as it is small and gentle.

◀ Dartmoor

Height: around 12.2 hands high (127 centimetres)
Colour: Bay, brown
Did you know? These ponies have lived wild on the moors of south-west England for hundreds of years.

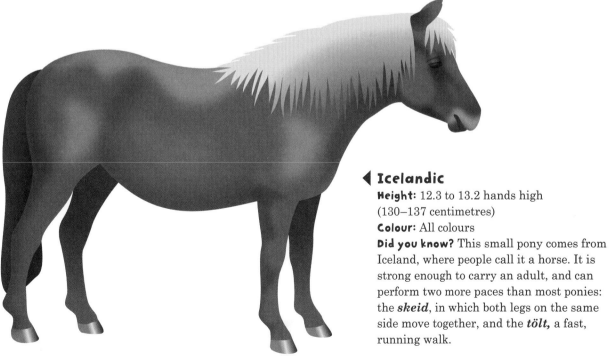

◀ Icelandic

Height: 12.3 to 13.2 hands high (130–137 centimetres)
Colour: All colours
Did you know? This small pony comes from Iceland, where people call it a horse. It is strong enough to carry an adult, and can perform two more paces than most ponies: the *skeid*, in which both legs on the same side move together, and the *tölt,* a fast, running walk.

61

More ponies

Caspian ▲
Height: 10 to 12 hands high (102–122 centimetres)
Colour: Usually bay or chestnut
Did you know? This small pony may be the oldest
breed in the world. It comes from Iran, and is
lightly built with a thin skin and a fine, silky coat.

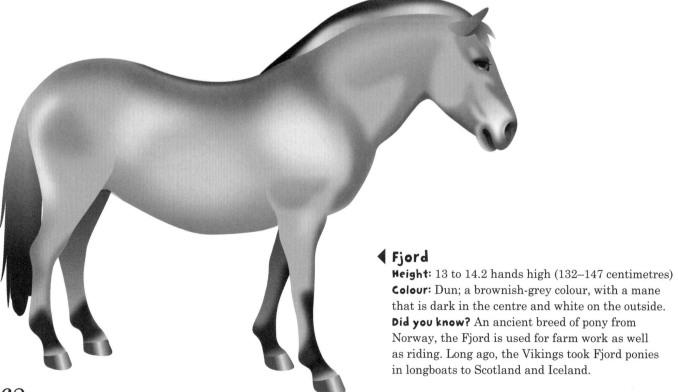

◀ Fjord
Height: 13 to 14.2 hands high (132–147 centimetres)
Colour: Dun; a brownish-grey colour, with a mane
that is dark in the centre and white on the outside.
Did you know? An ancient breed of pony from
Norway, the Fjord is used for farm work as well
as riding. Long ago, the Vikings took Fjord ponies
in longboats to Scotland and Iceland.

Haflinger ▼

Height: 13.1 to 14.2 hands high
(135–147 centimetres)
Colour: Chestnut or palomino
Did you know? The Haflinger is a strong pony
from Austria, used for riding, trekking and driving.
They can live until they are 40 years old.

Shetland ▲

Height: Shetlands are measured in inches –
up to 42 inches high (107 centimetres)
Colour: All colours
Did you know? The Shetland is the smallest of Britain's native
ponies. It comes from islands off the north-east coast of Scotland.
Shetlands are strong and very tough.

Connemara ▶

Height: 13 to 14.2 hands high
(137–147 centimetres)
Colour: Any solid colour
Did you know? This breed
comes from western Ireland.
It is fast, sure-footed and good
at jumping, making it a good
pony for riding in competitions.

63

Glossary

anvil – a heavy metal block on which hot horseshoes are hammered into shape.

arabesque – a balance on one leg, with the other leg stretched out straight behind.

barre – a rail or double rail attached to the wall of a ballet studio.

breeds – groups of horses and ponies with features in common.

character – a made-up person in a play or story.

chariot – a small, horse-drawn carriage.

choreographer – the person who puts dance moves together to form a ballet.

classical ballet – an older ballet technique from hundreds of years ago.

corps de ballet – dancers that perform together as a group.

curtsey – when a girl or woman bends her knees and bows her head.

dapple – light and dark hairs that form rings of colour on a pony's coat.

demi-plié – a half-bend at the knees.

dressage – advanced training of a ridden horse or pony.

emotions – feelings.

en pointe – standing raised on the tips of the toes wearing special shoes.

en tournant – a move which turns the dancer around.

eventing – a competition consisting of dressage, a cross-country course with jumps, and show jumping.

farrier – someone who shoes a horse or pony.

field shelter – a large open-fronted shed in a field.

gymkhana – an event with games and races performed on horseback.

hacking jacket – a smart wool jacket worn for riding.

hands high – horses and ponies are said to be so many "hands high". A hand is 10 centimetres or 4 inches.

horse – an animal over 14.2 hands high (147 centimetres).

jodhpurs – riding trousers with extra layers on the insides of the legs to stop rubbing from the saddle.

leotard – a special piece of stretchy clothing, a little like a swimsuit.

modern ballet – a type of ballet developed over the last hundred or so years.

pace – the way a horse or pony moves its legs at different speeds.

pirouette – a complete turn of the body on one foot.

plié – a bend at the knees.

pony – an animal up to and including 14.2 hands high (147 centimetres).

pose – a position a dancer stands in.

positions – five basic ways of placing the arms and feet in ballet.

posture – the way a dancer holds his or her body.

professional – when someone is fully trained to do something for a living.

rasp – a file used to smooth rough edges on a pony's hoof when it is being shod.

saddle soap – a special kind of soap that softens leather, used for cleaning tack.

soles – the undersides of the feet or bottom of shoes.

tack – the saddle, bridle and other equipment used on a riding pony.

tutu – a dress with a frilly net skirt worn in ballet.